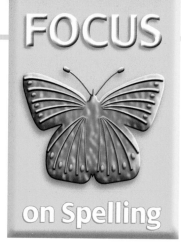

FOCUS
on Spelling

Spelling

Book 1

**Joyce Sweeney and
Carol Doncaster**

Collins

FOCUS
on Spelling

Using this book

This book will help you to develop good spelling strategies that you can use in your writing.

What's in a unit

Each unit is set out in the same way as the example here.

Unit heading
This tells you what you will be learning about.

Focus
This helps you think about the spelling rule.

More to think about
Activities to practise and develop your understanding.

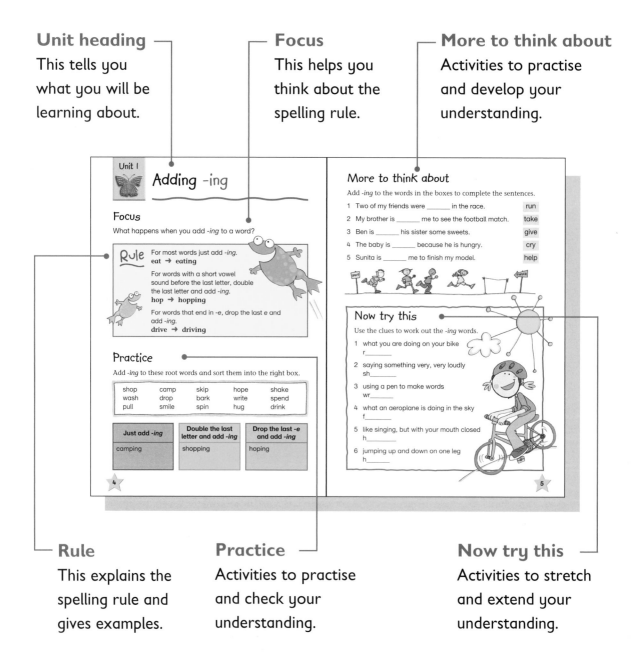

Unit 1

Adding -ing

Focus

What happens when you add *-ing* to a word?

Rule For most words just add *-ing*.
eat → eating

For words with a short vowel sound before the last letter, double the last letter and add *-ing*.
hop → hopping

For words that end in *-e*, drop the last *e* and add *-ing*.
drive → driving

Practice

Add *-ing* to these root words and sort them into the right box.

shop	camp	skip	hope	shake
wash	drop	bark	write	spend
pull	smile	spin	hug	drink

| Just add *-ing* | Double the last letter and add *-ing* | Drop the last *-e* and add *-ing* |
| camping | shopping | hoping |

4

More to think about

Add *-ing* to the words in the boxes to complete the sentences.

1 Two of my friends were _____ in the race. `run`
2 My brother is _____ me to see the football match. `take`
3 Ben is _____ his sister some sweets. `give`
4 The baby is _____ because he is hungry. `cry`
5 Sunita is _____ me to finish my model. `help`

Now try this

Use the clues to work out the *-ing* words.

1 what you are doing on your bike
   r_____
2 saying something very, very loudly
   sh_____
3 using a pen to make words
   wr_____
4 what an aeroplane is doing in the sky
   f_____
5 like singing, but with your mouth closed
   h_____
6 jumping up and down on one leg
   h_____

5

Rule
This explains the spelling rule and gives examples.

Practice
Activities to practise and check your understanding.

Now try this
Activities to stretch and extend your understanding.

Contents

Adding -ing

Focus

What happens when you add -ing to a word?

Rule

For most words just add -ing.

eat → **eating**

For words with a short vowel sound before the last letter, double the last letter and add -ing.

hop → **hopping**

For words that end in -e, drop the last e and add -ing.

drive → **driving**

Practice

Add -ing to these root words and sort them into the right box.

shop	camp	skip	hope	shake
wash	drop	bark	write	spend
pull	smile	spin	hug	drink

Just add -ing	Double the last letter and add -ing	Drop the last -e and add -ing
camping	shopping	hoping

4

More to think about

Add *-ing* to the words in the boxes to complete the sentences.

1 Two of my friends were _____ in the race.   run

2 My brother is _____ me to see the football match.   take

3 Ben is _____ his sister some sweets.   give

4 The baby is _____ because he is hungry.   cry

5 Sunita is _____ me to finish my model.   help

Now try this

Use the clues to work out the *-ing* words.

1 what you are doing on your bike
   r_____

2 saying something very, very loudly
   sh_____

3 using a pen to make words
   wr_____

4 what an aeroplane is doing in the sky
   f_____

5 like singing, but with your mouth closed
   h_____

6 jumping up and down on one leg
   h_____

5

Unit 2

Using -le

Focus

How do you spell words that end in -le?

Rule

After a long vowel sound, use *one* consonant + -le.
table

After a short vowel sound, use *two* consonants + -le.
bottle

Practice

1   Copy the table. Put the words below in the correct column.

tumble   table   giggle   saddle   jungle   cradle
beetle   needle   raffle   bubble   purple   scribble
little   steeple   poodle   candle   bundle   cable

Long vowel sound	Short vowel sound
needle	saddle

2   Now check the words in the table follow the spelling rule.

-   Long vowel words have one consonant + -le.
-   Short vowel words have two consonants + -le.

More to think about

Use the clues to write the words.
Check your answers in a dictionary.

1 to stand or walk in shallow water
   p_____

2 a seat on a bicycle
   s_____

3 a toy for a baby that makes a noise when it is shaken
   r_____

4 a piece of furniture with a flat top for putting things on
   t_____

Now try this

1 Write down the rhyming words in the poem.

   "Sit in your seat, don't jiggle,
   You're like an eel when you wriggle."
   Oh how his teacher liked to niggle
   When all James wanted was to giggle,
   Wriggle, jiggle and squiggle.

   Poem by Brian Moses

2 Now choose one of these rhyming patterns.

-istle	-ibble	-uckle	-imple
-ustle	-obble	-angle	-ickle

   Make a list of words that use your chosen rhyming
   pattern. Write a short rhyme, using a rhyming
   dictionary to help you.

Using un-, de-, dis-, re- and pre-

Focus

What is a prefix? What does it do? Let's look at the prefixes *un-*, *de-*, *dis-*, *re-* and *pre-*.

> ### Rule
> A prefix is a group of letters added to the beginning of a word.
> A prefix changes the meaning of a word.

Practice

Add *un-* or *dis-* to each word to make a new word.
Circle the prefix.

| un- | dis- |

1   happy   (un)happy   2   obey   _____

3   well   _____   4   appear   _____

5   fit   _____   6   like   _____

More to think about

Use the clues to write the words.
You can use a dictionary to help you.

1 when someone leaves a place
   de_____

2 when you do not agree with someone
   dis_____

3 when you take everything out of a suitcase
   un_____

4 to come back to a place after you have been away
   re_____

5 a group of letters added to the beginning of a word
   to make a new word
   pre_____

Now try this

| dis- | re- | un- |

1 Add the right prefix to make a new word.

   a) equal   b) honest   c) move

2 Now use each new word in a sentence.

Progress test 1

A Write the correct *-ing* word for each picture.

1

w_____

2

r_____

3

p_____

4

c_____

5

d_____

6

h_____

B These words end with *-le*. Write the words.

1

k_____

2

c_____

3

b_____

4

t_____

5

n_____

6

b_____

C Choose the correct prefix for each word.
Use a dictionary to check your answers.

1 *de-* or *pre-*   _____historic

2 *dis-* or *un-*   _____agree

3 *de-* or *un-*   _____tie

4 *un-* or *re-*   _____place

5 *pre-* or *un-*   _____fair   7 *un-* or *re-*   _____cycle

6 *dis-* or *re-*   _____honest   8 *de-* or *un-*   _____part

D Find ten words in this wordsearch. Each word should end in
-ing, -le or have a prefix. Write the words.

d	i	g	g	i	n	g	a	n	l
b	h	a	n	d	l	e	c	g	i
d	i	s	l	i	k	e	h	m	p
k	q	t	w	o	b	b	l	e	n
j	z	u	n	k	i	n	d	w	u
g	i	g	g	l	e	z	o	c	a
d	r	n	r	r	e	t	u	r	n
c	o	m	i	n	g	a	w	v	l
p	b	s	t	a	r	t	i	n	g
s	m	x	t	i	c	k	l	e	b

Well done – you've finished your progress test.

Homophones

Focus

Did you know that some words sound the same but have different spellings?

 Rule Words that sound the same but have different spellings, like *there* and *their,* are called homophones.

There answers the question "Where?"
The book is over *there*.

Their shows when something belongs to someone.
The twins have lost *their* dog.

Here are some ways to help you remember how to spell *there* and *their*.

● *There* and *their* both start with *the*.
● *There* looks like *where*.
● Remember this sentence to help you spell *their*:
  Their hedgehog eats insect ravioli!

Practice

Choose the correct word to complete the sentences.

| their | there |

1 You can park your car over _____.

2 We are going to _____ house to watch a video.

3 We are going over _____ to play football.

4 They have lost _____ tickets for the match.

More to think about

These can also be tricky words to spell:

to	too	two

Here are some ways to help you remember how to spell them.

- *To* is used most often.
  He went *to* the zoo.

- *Two* is the number 2.
  A bird has *two* wings.

  t w o
  two **w**ings **o**nly

- *Too* means "more than enough".
  It is *too* heavy.

- *Too* can also mean "as well as".
  The dog came *too*.

Choose the correct word to complete the sentences.

1 I felt _____ hot in the sun.

2 Number _____ comes before number three.

3 The children ran _____ school.

4 There are _____ samosas left.

Now try this

Finish the report, choosing the missing words.

to	too	two	there	their

The _____ girls were getting ready _____ go _____

school. They put on _____ scarves and _____ mittens

_____. After a _____-minute walk, they were _____!

Adding -er and -est

Focus

What happens when you add -er and -est to a word?

Rule Most words just add -er and -est.
long → longer → longest

For words ending in -e, take off the final -e and add -er and -est.
close → closer → closest

After a short vowel sound, double the final letter and add -er and -est.
fit → fitter → fittest

Practice

1 Copy the table. Add -er or -est to each word.
   Remember to check if the vowel sound is long or short.

Word	Add -er	Add -est
hot	hotter	hottest
quick		
ripe		
clean		

2 Copy and complete the sentences.

   a) The road is _____ than the pavement.   (wider/widest)

   b) March was the _____ month of the year. (wetter/wettest)

   c) She built the_____ snowman in town.   (bigger/biggest)

More to think about

Copy and complete the sentences.
Use the pictures to help.

1   Emma is _____ than Laura.

2   Laura is _____ than Emma.

3   Alan is the _____ .

4   Richard is _____ than Clare.

5   The hare is _____ than the tortoise.

6   The tortoise is _____ than the hare.

Now try this

| sad | thin | strong | big |

Choose one of the words above, or use one of your own.
Draw three pictures to show how adding -er and -est
changes the meaning.
Then write a sentence about each picture.

Adding -y

Focus

What happens when you add -y to a word?

Rule   Most words just add -y.
sleep → **sleepy**

For words ending in -e, take off the final -e and add -y.
laze → **lazy**

After a short vowel sound, double the final consonant and add -y.
fur → **furry**

Practice

1   Add -y to each word, and write the new words.

chill	grump	noise	bend	fun	shine
ice	nut	mess	run	grease	snap

2   Copy and complete the sentences,
using the new words.

   c) The car skidded on the _____ road.

   b) The _____ man shouted at the children.

   c) The boys were asked to tidy their _____ room.

   d) The film was very _____ .

More to think about

Read the clues and write the words.

1 covered in wet, sticky earth   m_____ y

2 covered with dust   d_____ y

3 a ball is this   b_____ y

4 reddish-pink in colour   r_____ y

5 needing a drink   th_____ y

Now try this

Write a paragraph about a clown.
Describe him or her using at least four of the words below.
Use other interesting words of your own.

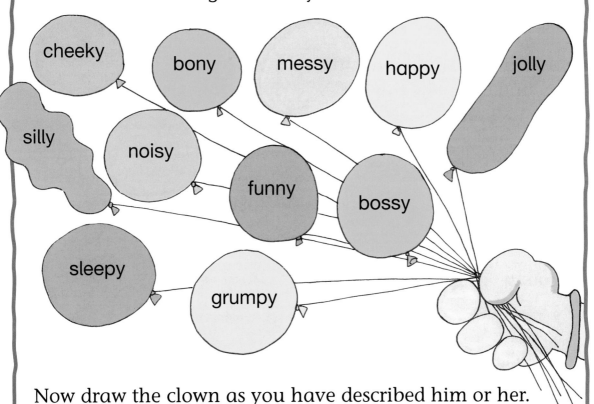

cheeky
bony
messy
happy
jolly
silly
noisy
funny
bossy
sleepy
grumpy

Now draw the clown as you have described him or her.

Unit 7

Changing -y to -er or -est

Focus

What happens when you add *-er* or *-est* to a word like *funny*?

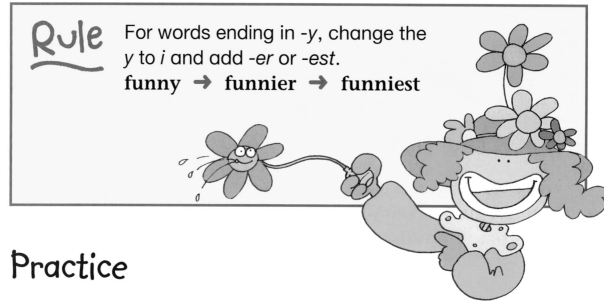

Rule

For words ending in *-y*, change the y to *i* and add *-er* or *-est*.

funny → **funnier** → **funniest**

Practice

Add *-er* and *-est* to change the root words.
Copy and complete the table.

cloudy	frilly	silly	grumpy
merry	happy	messy	bossy
pretty	naughty	tasty	noisy

Root word	Add *-er*	Add *-est*
cloudy	cloudier	cloudiest

More to think about

Copy and complete the sentences using *-er* and *-est* words.

1 The pantomime was the _____ I had ever seen.   funny

2 It is _____ today than it was yesterday.   chilly

3 Ajay's bicycle is the _____ in the street.   shiny

4 Mum says I have the _____ socks in the world.   smelly

Now try this

1 Complete the sentences with *-er* or *-est* words.

happy

Yasir is _____ .

Yasir

Ben

heavy

The box is _____ .

sunny

Wednesday was _____ .

Monday   Tuesday   Wednesday

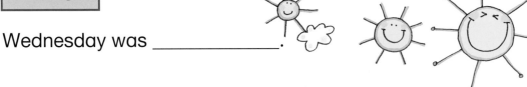

2 Choose a root word from the Practice section.
   Draw three pictures to show how adding *-er* and *-est*
   changes the meaning. Then write a sentence about
   each picture.

Adding -s and -es

Focus

What happens when you change a word into a plural by adding -s and -es?

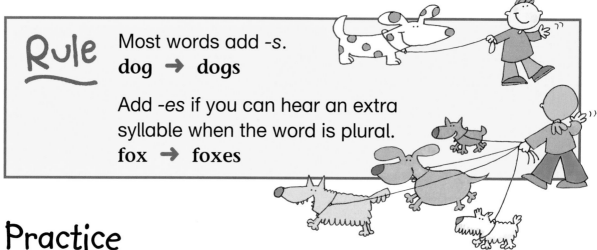

Rule   Most words add -s.
dog → dogs

Add -es if you can hear an extra syllable when the word is plural.
fox → foxes

Practice

1   Copy and complete the list of all the items in the cupboard.

3 glasses
1 hat

More to think about

Copy and complete the sentences.

plate

match

van

box

bush

1 Three _____ arrived at the garage.

2 The _____ were too heavy to lift.

3 The _____ are on the top shelf.

4 The _____ had become overgrown.

5 _____ should be kept in a safe place.

Now try this

Rewrite these signs correctly.

1 Buy three bookes, get one *free!*

2 Buy two bunchs of rose and get the third bunch half price!

3 **Bargain!**
Two dresss for the price of one!

4 Six bottlees of cola for the price of five!

5 Free chipes with every burger!

Progress test 2

A Add *-er* or *-est* to each word.

1
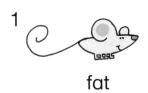  

fat   _____   _____

2

tall   _____   _____

3

big   _____   _____

4

ripe   _____   _____

5

long   _____   _____

B Add -y to change these words.

1 smell

2 bone

3 grump

4 squeak

5 fog

6 wave

C Write the correct plurals for each picture.

1

2

3

4

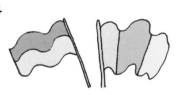

5

6

7

8

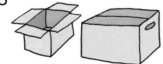

9

Well done – you've finished your progress test.

23

Silent letters

Focus

Did you know that some words have silent letters?

Rule Silent *g* and silent *k* can be found before *n*.
gnat **k**nee

Silent *w* sometimes comes before *r*.
wrap

Silent *b* sometimes comes after *m*.
lam**b**

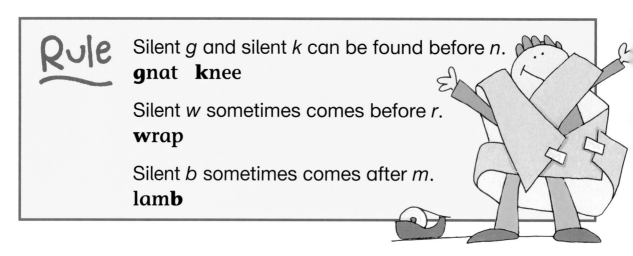

Practice

Write the correct word for each picture.
Circle the silent letter in each word.

1

2

3

4

5

6

7

8

9

More to think about

Use the clues to write the words.
Check your answers in a dictionary.

1   a man in armour who rode into battle for his king or queen

2   where your leg bends

3   a line that forms on your skin as you grow old

4   joints where your fingers bend

5   a baby sheep

Now try this

Find ten words with silent letters in this wordsearch.
Six words go across and four words go down.

a	k	n	u	c	k	l	e
k	n	i	t	d	d	a	k
h	o	w	j	p	d	m	n
u	c	r	u	m	b	b	i
x	k	o	d	d	d	i	f
y	k	n	e	e	l	z	e
l	s	g	n	o	m	e	p
w	r	i	n	k	l	e	q

Compound words

Focus

What are compound words? How do you make them?

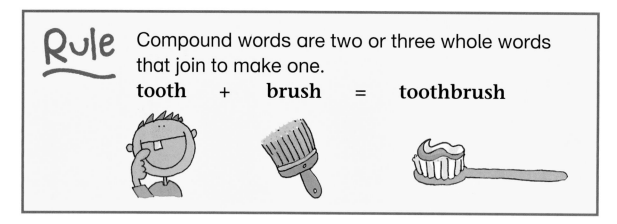

Rule Compound words are two or three whole words that join to make one.

tooth   +   brush   =   toothbrush

Practice

Choose a word from column 1 and a word from column 2 to make a compound word. Write the words and the compound word, like this:

fire   +   fighter   =   firefighter

Column 1	Column 2
fire	nail
tea	room
head	fighter
toe	bow
cloak	pot
water	fall
back	pack
rain	light

More to think about

Write a compound word beginning with each of the following words.

1 tooth_____

2 dust_____

3 post_____

4 rain_____

5 hair_____

6 sea_____

7 door_____

8 any_____

9 some_____

10 short_____

11 foot_____

12 grand_____

Now try this

How many compound words can you make using the picture clues? You can use some words more than once.

butter

Common suffixes

Focus

What is a suffix? What does it do? Let's look at the suffixes -*ly*, -*ful* and -*less*.

 A suffix is a group of letters added at the end of a word.
A suffix changes the meaning of a word.
Some common suffixes are -*ly*, -*ful* and -*less*.

Tariq is friendly.
Steve's foot is painful.
Tom is careless.

Practice

1   Add the suffix to change the words below.
    Write the new words and underline the suffix.

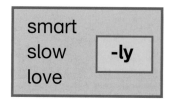
smart
slow   **-ly**
love

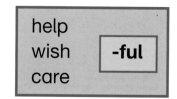
help
wish   **-ful**
care

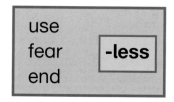
use
fear   **-less**
end

2   Copy and complete the sentences, choosing one word from each group above.

a) The bus went _____ up the steep hill.

b) The children were _____ when they crossed the road.

c) The path up the mountain seemed _____.

More to think about

Write words that end with *-ly, -ful* or *-less* to complete the sentences.

1   Vikram was _____ when he won the prize.   speech

2   The new pupil was dressed _____.   smart

3   The blunt knife was _____ for chopping.   use

4   We had a _____ holiday with friends.   wonder

5   Susan was very _____ when Gran was ill.   help

6   The mess was _____ cleared up.   quick

Now try this

Write a paragraph about Jack, using at least five of the words below.
Use other words with suffixes to make the paragraph interesting.

friendly   smartly

careful   thoughtful

fearless   **Jack**   forgetful

careless   homeless

helpful

successful   wonderful

Now draw Jack as you have described him.

29

Contractions 1

Focus

What does the apostrophe (') mean in words like *I'm*?

Rule An apostrophe (') is used where two words have been joined and some letters missed out. The shortened word is called a contraction.

I am → **I'm**

Practice

1 Copy these contractions. Then write each one out in full.

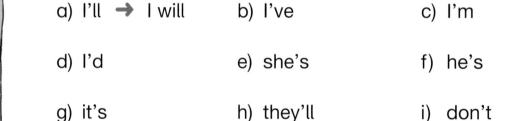

a) I'll → I will   b) I've   c) I'm

d) I'd   e) she's   f) he's

g) it's   h) they'll   i) don't

j) can't   k) isn't   l) doesn't

2 Now choose three contractions and use each one in a sentence.

More to think about

Use apostrophes to shorten and join together the underlined words in these sentences.

1 <u>He is</u> waiting for his dad by the bus stop.

2 <u>I am</u> sorry that you are not coming to my party.

3 <u>She is</u> not going to play football today.

4 <u>I have</u> lost my purse.

5 <u>There is</u> a bee in the kitchen.

6 Bill <u>does not</u> want to see that film.

Now try this

Rewrite these signs correctly.

1 Ive gone for lunch. Ill be back in an hour.

2 Our prices cant be beaten!

3 Its time for a change.

4 Dont play football on the grass!

5 Feeding the animals isnt allowed!

6 Try this – youll be amazed at the results.

Progress test 3

A Write the correct words. Each has a silent letter.

1

2

3

4

5

6

7

8

9

B Write the compound words.

1

2

3

4

5

6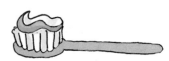

C Add the suffixes *-ly, -ful* or *-less* to change these words.

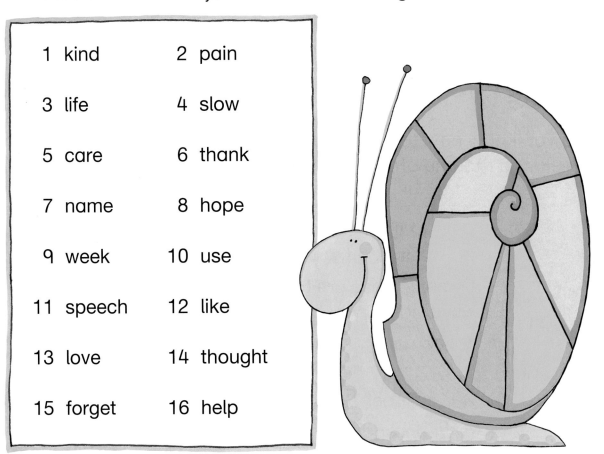

1 kind	2 pain
3 life	4 slow
5 care	6 thank
7 name	8 hope
9 week	10 use
11 speech	12 like
13 love	14 thought
15 forget	16 help

D Put the apostrophe in the correct place in these contractions.

1 cant	2 doesnt	3 Im	4 shes
5 dont	6 isnt	7 Ill	8 theyll
9 its	10 well	11 wont	12 theres
13 wasnt	14 shell	15 Ive	16 hes

Well done – you've finished your progress test.

Days, weeks and months

Focus

Do you know how to spell the days of the week and months of the year?

> **Rule**   Days of the week and months of the year must start with a capital letter.
>
> Some of these are tricky words. Here are some ways to help you to remember the tricky spellings.
>
> - February   In your head say *Feb – ru – ary* to help you remember the first *r*.
> - December   Don't be a fool, December is cool!
> - Wednesday   In your head say *Wed – nes – day*.
> - Make up your own ways of remembering.
> - Use the "Look, Say, Cover, Write, Check" method.

Practice

Complete the sentences. Harry should do something on each day of the week.

1   Harry sent an email on __Monday__ .
2   Harry went to the park on _____.
3   Harry went shopping on _____.
4   Harry read his book on _____.
5   Harry went to the cinema on _____.
6   Harry played chess on _____.
7   Harry watched a video on _____.

More to think about

1 Use the clues to work out the names of all 12 months.

    a) The first month of the year.
    b) Bonfire Night is on the 5th of this month.
    c) A summer month with one syllable and four letters.
    d) People play practical jokes on the first day of this month.
    e) This month comes after September and before November.
    f) The last month of the year.
    g) This month has 28 days, but 29 in each leap year.
    h) This is the third month of the year and has 31 days.
    i) This can be a name for a girl and it has three letters.
    j) A summer month, the first letter is J and it has two syllables.
    k) This is the ninth month of the year and comes before October.
    l) Another summer month, this one has a tricky spelling.

2 Now write the months in the correct order.

1 January

Now try this

Read this poem.
Then choose a month and write a poem in the same way.

April means short sharp showers
Pouring from the sky,
Ruining hopes of outdoor play.
It's almost, but not quite summer
Leading onto drier May.

Poem by Brian Moses

Short words inside long words

Focus

When does a long word have a short word inside it?

 Rule The letters of the shorter words must appear consecutively (together).
elephant *ant* is a shorter word, but *pant* is not

Practice

How many smaller words can you find in the words below?
Copy and write the words in the table.

screwdriver	screw, driver, drive, river, crew
blackboard	
forgetful	
playground	
information	
knowledge	
paintbrush	

More to think about

The is a very important word.

1   Write down five words that have *the* at the beginning, for example **the**y.

2   Write down five words that have *the* inside them, for example pan**the**r.

Now try this

On the labels, write the short name (or names) for each person.

1   Benjamin
   Ben

2   Alexander

3   Robert

4   Suzanne

5   Sunita

6   Elizabeth

7   Rajinder

8   Samuel

9   William

Common prefixes

Focus

What is a prefix? What does it do? Let's look at the prefixes
mis-, *non-*, *ex-*, *co-* and *anti-*.

> $R\underline{ule}$ A prefix is a group of letters added to the
> beginning of a word.
> A prefix changes the meaning of a word.

Practice

Add a prefix to each word to make a new word.
Circle the prefix.

| mis- | anti- | non- |

1   February ✔   Febuary ✘

    spell   (mis) spell

2

    clockwise   _____

3   $4 + 3 = 7$ ✔ $4 + 3 = 6$ ✘

    calculate   _____

4

    sense   _____

5

    behave   _____

6

    fiction   _____

More to think about

Write the meanings of these words. Check your answers in a dictionary.

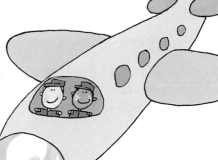

1 copilot

2 mislead

3 antiseptic

4 nonsense

5 misbehave

6 anticlockwise

7 coeducation

Now try this

The prefixes *anti-* and *non-* are often used in advertising.

antiwrinkle

nonstick

anti- means *against*

non- means *not* (the opposite)

Design an advertisement using the prefixes *anti-* or *non-*. Use one of the words below or one of your own.

rust	drip	slip	stop
stick	frizz	racism	smoking

Contractions 2

Focus

What does the apostrophe (') mean in words like *you're*?

 An apostrophe (') is used where two words have been joined and some letters missed out.
The shortened word is called a contraction.

you are ➜ **you're**

Practice

1 Copy these contractions. Then write each one out in full.

a) we're	b) she'll	c) couldn't	d) they're
e) shouldn't	f) hadn't	g) you'll	h) we'll
i) haven't	j) they'll	k) you're	l) aren't

2 Now copy all the words into the table.

Missing *a*	Missing *wi*	Missing *o*
we're (we are)	she'll (she will)	couldn't (could not)

More to think about

Use apostrophes to shorten and join together the underlined words in these sentences.

1   I <u>could not</u> find my key.

2   <u>She has</u> plenty of money for her ticket.

3   <u>We are</u> all going to the cinema.

4   <u>We will</u> go by bus to the airport.

5   <u>They have</u> been swimming at the sports centre.

6   <u>She is</u> running in the race today.

Now try this

1   Contractions are often used in advertising. What contraction is used in each of these advertisements?

Write the contraction. Now write the words in full.

2   Design an advertisement using the contraction *'n'*.

Homonyms

Focus

Homonyms are words that have the same spelling but different meanings.

> **Rule** The text *around* the word explains the meaning.
> The runner needs to **train** every day.
> The **train** left the station at 10:30.

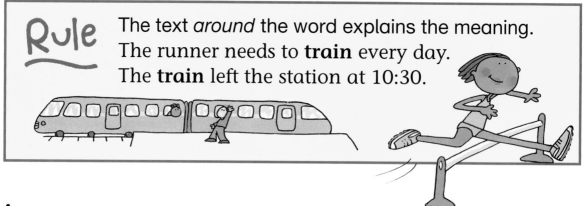

Practice

Choose the correct word to complete the sentences.

ring	lift	bank	palm

1 I held the ladybird in the _____ of my hand.

   The coconut fell from the _____ tree.

2 My _____ slipped off my finger.

   The bell will _____ at nine o'clock.

3 We sat on the _____ of the river.

   I have no money left in the _____.

4 We took the _____ to the top floor.

   The box is too heavy to _____.

More to think about

| fly | book | match |

1 Illustrate the words in the boxes in two different ways to show their two different meanings, like this:

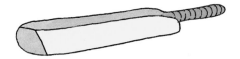

bat

2 Write two sentences for each of the words above, showing their two different meanings.

Now try this

Look at the picture above and find five homonyms.
Write the words to show that they have different meanings.

1 <u>bow</u> in hair   <u>bow</u> and arrow

Question words

Focus

What are question words? When do you use a question mark?

Rule	Sentences that start with a question word must have a question mark (?) at the end. **What** is your name?

Practice

who

when

why

how

where

what

1 Look at the question words above. Say each word. Think about the tricky parts. Cover each word in turn and write it.

2 Copy and complete the questions.

a) ____Why____ did you choose a red car?

b) _____ rang the doorbell?

c) _____ will we do tomorrow?

d) _____ is the nearest petrol station?

e) _____ will the train arrive?

f) _____ many people are staying for lunch?

More to think about

Write questions for these answers. Use the words in boxes to start your questions.

1 I went to buy a CD.   why

2 It is six o'clock.   what

3 It starts at 10 o'clock.   when

4 I'm fine, thank you.   how

5 I live in Newcastle.   where

6 I will ask Seema and Brian to come.   who

Don't forget to start your question with a capital letter.

Now try this

There has been a robbery at the shop.
Write five questions that the police officer might ask the shopkeeper.

Progress test 4

A How many smaller words can you find in the words below? Copy the table and write down the smaller words.

grandad	
information	
bridegroom	
standstill	
together	

B Use the clues to write the words. Each word starts with one of the prefixes shown below.

mis-	non-	ex-	co-	anti-

1 a person who shares the flying of a plane

2 to spell a word wrongly

3 silly words that don't mean anything

4 moving in the opposite direction to the hands of a clock

5 to swap something for something else

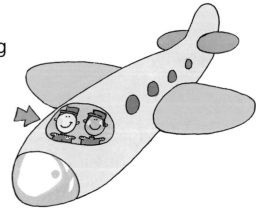

C Write the contractions.

1 cannot   2 she is   3 could not

4 we will   5 have not   6 we are

7 does not   8 he had   9 it is

D Use the clues to write the correct homonym.

patient	pen	jam

1 food that you spread on bread

2 a person who is ill in hospital

3 a small fenced area in which farm animals are kept

4 able to wait without complaining

5 an instrument for writing with

6 where there is so much traffic that cars cannot move

E Use the question words to complete the sentences. Don't forget to start your question with a capital letter.

who	what	when	where	how	why

1 _____ ate all the samosas?   4 _____ would you like to do?

2 _____ is my camera?   5 _____ will you be ready?

3 _____ are you feeling?   6 _____ is the sky blue?

Well done – you've finished your progress test.

47

Spellchecker

A Write the words.

1

She is s_____.

2

a c_____

3

the b_____ rock

4

a c_____

5

two w_____

6

a c_____

B Write the signs correctly for the swimming pool.
Then check the spellings in your dictionary.

1 No diveing

2 Riturn locker keys

3 Changing Roomes

4 Gogles £5

5 Dont run. Wet floors.

Well done – you've finished your Spellchecker.

48